Table of Contents

O9-BTI-897

Student Name: _Jeffrey Torres_ Notebook Number: _____

Email: _____ Phone: _____

Network ID: _____ Course: _Chm 2046_

Lab Instructor: _Larry Chamusco_ Section: _003_ Semester: _Spring 2020_

Lab Partners: _____

Date	Experiment/Subject	Page Number

Table of Contents

Date	Experiment/Subject	Page Number

124 s

Run 4

Elapsed times	Absorbance		Temperature
70 s	0.51	70 s	2.055
90 s	0.551	90 s	7.011
95 s	0.516	95 s	1.95
115 s	0.465	90 s	1.223
135 s	0.425	115 s	1.021
165 s	0.381	170 s	1.313
180 s	0.365	160 s	1.183
117 s	0.334	185 s	0.979
120 s	0.295	180 s	0.843
210 s	0.270	300 s	0.843
220 s	0.243	720 s	0.512
240 s	0.230	740 s	0.410
200 s	0.199	200 s	
280 s	0.18	220 s	
300 s	0.163	300 s	
320 s	0.146	320 s	
360 s	0.132	340 s	
350 s	0.118	300 s	
380 s	0.105	380 s	
420 s	0.091		
470 s	0.079		
440 s	0.075		
500 s	0.060		

Data   Analysis

Tubes	Absorbance
1	0.147
2	0.118
3	0.214
4	0.110
5	0.165

Data   Analysis

Index	Absorbance
1	0.147
2	0.113
3	0.214
4	0.110
5	0.165

COPY

Name	Lab Partner	Locker/ Desk No.	Course & Section No.

COPY

THE HAYDEN-McNEIL STUDENT LAB NOTEBOOK   Note: Insert Divider Under Copy Sheet Before Writing

THE HAYDEN-McNEIL STUDENT LAB NOTEBOOK

Note: Insert Divider Under Copy Sheet Before Writing

THE HAYDEN-McNEIL STUDENT LAB NOTEBOOK

Note: Insert Divider Under Copy Sheet Before Writing

COPY

THE HAYDEN-McNEIL STUDENT LAB NOTEBOOK

Note: Insert Divider Under Copy Sheet Before Writing

THE HAYDEN-MCNEIL STUDENT LAB NOTEBOOK

Note: Insert Divider Under Copy Sheet Before Writing

Note: Insert Divider Under Copy Sheet Before Writing

COPY

THE HAYDEN-McNEIL STUDENT LAB NOTEBOOK

Note: Insert Divider Under Copy Sheet Before Writing

Name	Lab Partner	Locker/ Desk No.	Course & Section No.

Signature	Date	Witness/TA	Date

Name	Lab Partner	Locker/ Desk No.	Course & Section No.

Signature	Date	Witness/TA	Date

Signature		Date	Witness/TA		Date

THE HAYDEN-McNEIL STUDENT LAB NOTEBOOK   Note: Insert Divider Under Copy Sheet Before Writing

THE HAYDEN-McNEIL STUDENT LAB NOTEBOOK   Note: Insert Divider Under Copy Sheet Before Writing

Name	Lab Partner	Locker/ Desk No.	Course & Section No.

THE HAYDEN-McNEIL STUDENT LAB NOTEBOOK

Note: Insert Divider Under Copy Sheet Before Writing

Exp. No.	Experiment/Subject		Date	
Name	Lab Partner		Locker/ Desk No.	Course & Section No.

Signature		Date	Witness/TA		Date

Note: Insert Divider Under Copy Sheet Before Writing

Exp. No.	Experiment/Subject		Date	
Name	Lab Partner		Locker/Desk No.	Course & Section No.

COPY

Signature		Date	Witness/TA		Date

Note: Insert Divider Under Copy Sheet Before Writing

Exp. No.	Experiment/Subject		Date	22
Name	Lab Partner		Locker/ Desk No.	Course & Section No.

Signature		Date	Witness/TA		Date

Note: Insert Divider Under Copy Sheet Before Writing

Note: Insert Divider Under Copy Sheet Before Writing

Name	Lab Partner	Locker/ Desk No.	Course & Section No.

Signature		Date	Witness/TA		Date

THE HAYDEN-McNEIL STUDENT LAB NOTEBOOK

Note: Insert Divider Under Copy Sheet Before Writing

COPY

THE HAYDEN-McNEIL STUDENT LAB NOTEBOOK   Note: Insert Divider Under Copy Sheet Before Writing

| Name | Lab Partner | Locker/ Desk No. | Course & Section No. |

| Signature | | Date | Witness/TA | | Date |

Name	Lab Partner	Locker/Desk No.	Course & Section No.

Signature	Date	Witness/TA	Date

COPY

THE HAYDEN-McNEIL STUDENT LAB NOTEBOOK

Note: Insert Divider Under Copy Sheet Before Writing

COPY

THE HAYDEN-McNEIL STUDENT LAB NOTEBOOK   Note: Insert Divider Under Copy Sheet Before Writing

Name	Lab Partner	Locker/ Desk No.	Course & Section No.

Signature	Date	Witness/TA	Date

THE HAYDEN-McNEIL STUDENT LAB NOTEBOOK

Note: Insert Divider Under Copy Sheet Before Writing

COPY

THE HAYDEN-McNEIL STUDENT LAB NOTEBOOK   Note: Insert Divider Under Copy Sheet Before Writing

Exp. No.	Experiment/Subject		Date	
Name	Lab Partner		Locker/ Desk No.	Course & Section No.

Signature		Date	Witness/TA		Date

THE HAYDEN-McNEIL STUDENT LAB NOTEBOOK   Note: Insert Divider Under Copy Sheet Before Writing

COPY

THE HAYDEN-McNEIL STUDENT LAB NOTEBOOK

Note: Insert Divider Under Copy Sheet Before Writing

Exp. No.	Experiment/Subject		Date	
Name	Lab Partner		Locker/ Desk No.	Course & Section No.

Signature		Date	Witness/TA		Date

Name	Lab Partner	Locker/ Desk No.	Course & Section No.

Signature	Date	Witness/TA	Date

COPY

THE HAYDEN-McNEIL STUDENT LAB NOTEBOOK   Note: Insert Divider Under Copy Sheet Before Writing

Exp. No.	Experiment/Subject		Date	
Name	Lab Partner		Locker/Desk No.	Course & Section No.

Signature		Date	Witness/TA		Date

COPY

THE HAYDEN-McNEIL STUDENT LAB NOTEBOOK

Note: Insert Divider Under Copy Sheet Before Writing

Name	Lab Partner	Locker/ Desk No.	Course & Section No.

Signature	Date	Witness/TA	Date

Signature		Date	Witness/TA		Date

| Name | Lab Partner | Locker/
Desk No. | Course &
Section No. |

| Signature | | Date | Witness/TA | | Date |

Note: Insert Divider Under Copy Sheet Before Writing

COPY

THE HAYDEN-McNEIL STUDENT LAB NOTEBOOK

Note: Insert Divider Under Copy Sheet Before Writing

COPY

COPY

Note: Insert Divider Under Copy Sheet Before Writing

COPY

Signature		Date	Witness/TA		Date

THE HAYDEN-McNEIL STUDENT LAB NOTEBOOK

Note: Insert Divider Under Copy Sheet Before Writing

COPY

THE HAYDEN-McNEIL STUDENT LAB NOTEBOOK   Note: Insert Divider Under Copy Sheet Before Writing